Arab

Thoroughbred

Friesian

Dartmoor

Lusitano

Lipizzaner

Mustang

Piebald

Shire

Falabella

Appaloosa

Shetland Pony

Palomino

Norwegian fjord pony

Breton

Pinto

Walking

Trotting

Cantering

Galloping

Jumping

Eating grass

Rearing

Tethered

circus horse

Whinnying

Prehistoric horse

Horse and rosette

Dressage horse

Bridled horse

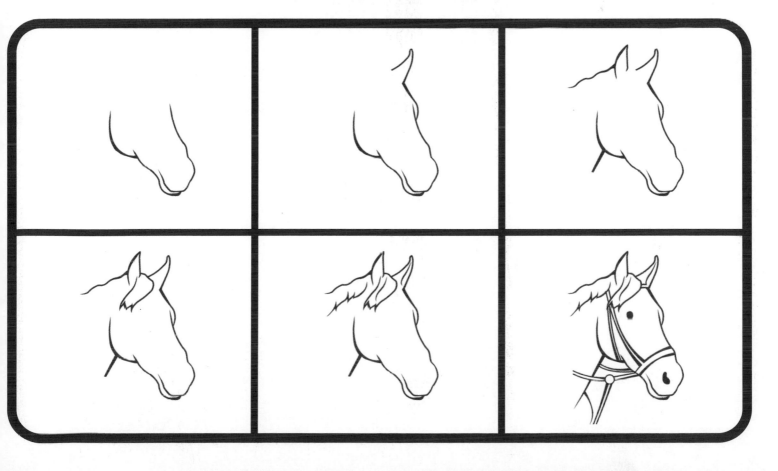

Bucking bronco with rider

Polo pony with rider

Mother and foal

Racehorse with blinkers

Medieval tournament horse

Expression; ears forward

Expression; ears back

Harness racing

classical equitation

Eventing horse

Two heads nuzzling

Show horse

fantasy horse - unicorn head

fantasy horse - pegasus full body

fantasy horse - pegasus head

fantasy horse - unicorn full body

Mustang close-up

Thoroughbred close-up

Piebald pony

Eating hay

Plaited tail

Plaited mane

Horse in horsebox

Rear view of saddle

Horse lying down

Horse rolling over

Horse pawing the ground

Horse with blanket

Foal

Horse being re-shod

Horse led with halter

Police horse

Jockey on horse

Canadian Mountie horse

Horse drinking

Horse guards

Horse with Western saddle

Horses with nose markings

Show jumping

foal suckling mother

Play fighting

Horse jumping a countryside fence

Horse trotting with rider

Buck-toothed cartoon horse

cartoon pony

cartoon seahorse

cartoon pegasus

cartoon horse - galloping

cool horse

cool pony

cartoon foal - Cantering

cartoon old horse

Pop star pony

cartoon horse - flower in mouth

Horse over stable door

Horse - rear view

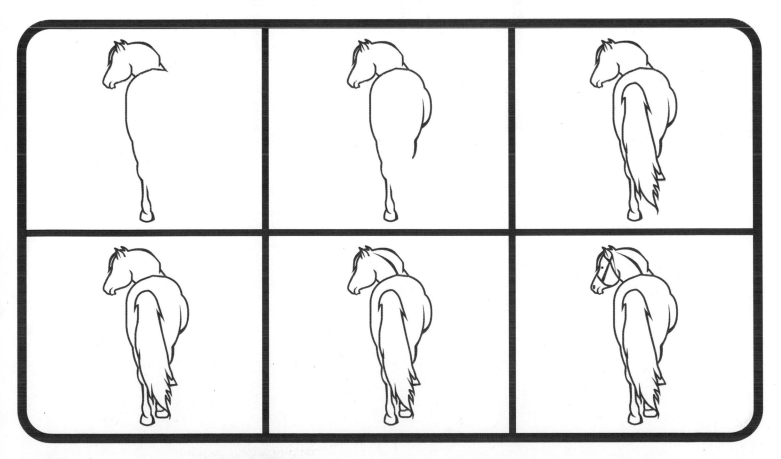

Jockey

Bucking horse

Horse Cantering through water

Horse high-trotting

Cowboy

Horse Chewing

Petting

Horse and cart

Horses fighting

Wild Horses

Miniature

Horse with Native American

Peering

Horse with Blaze

Leisure rider